brother

_____

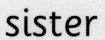

sister

_____

baby

_____

boy

_____

girl

_____

happy

sad

shy

tall

eyes

_____

ears

_____

face

_____

nose

_____

mouth

_____

Let's cook!

milk

_____

water

_____

glass

_____

cup

_____

drink

_____

spoon

_____

corn

_____

tin

_____

apple

_____

cook   like

eat   drink

pan

_____

hot

cold

sweet

ripe

cake

_____

eggs

_____

plate

_____

box

_____

cheese

_____

bag

_____

bread

_____

Come outside

ball

_____

tree

_____

bike

_____

bird

_____

wheel

_____

boat

_____

jump

drive

run

go

sea

_____

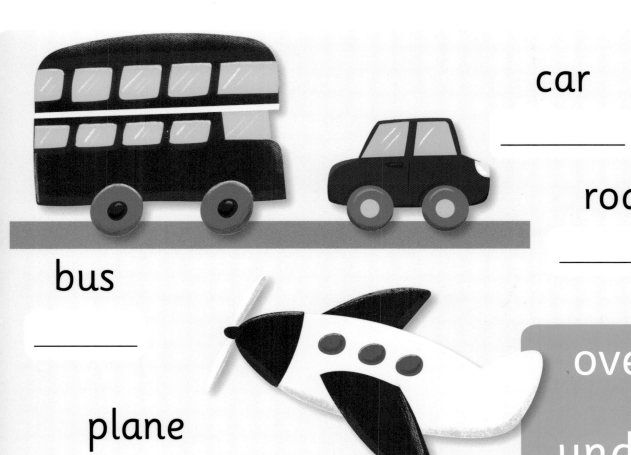

car

_____

road

_____

bus

_____

over

under

fast

high

plane

_____

rain

_____

cloud

_____

sun

_____

kite

_____

sky

_____

At home

house
_____

roof
_____

door
_____

boots
_____

hat
_____

coat
_____

bath
_____

socks
_____

sit   lie

read   watch

computer

_____

lamp

_____

table

_____

book

_____

doll

_____

bed

_____

teddy

_____

here
there
happy
tired

train

_____

Animals

dog

frog

lead

collar

bark

walk fly

play

shark

mane

horse

cow

duck

_____

cat

_____

mouse

_____

sheep

_____

hen

_____

tail

_____

seal

_____

lion

_____

little   big

black   white

At school

paper

_____

pencil

_____

desk

_____

glasses

_____

ask

say

learn

think

$$2 + 2 =$$
$$7 \times 3 =$$

teacher

_____

1 2 3

numbers

_____

clock

_____

kind
funny
brave
loud

music
_____

drum
_____

stick
_____

map
_____

triangle
_____

paints
_____

People at work

tractor
_____

farmer
_____

make

help

fix

use

train
_____

farm
_____

keeper
_____

zoo
_____

tracks
_____

job
_____

driver
_____

fire
_____

ladder
_____

truck
_____

hose
_____

nurse
_____

suit
_____

letter
_____

city
_____

case
_____

post
_____

old   new

sick   well

mail
_____

Wipe Clean
First Words

Have fun completing the activities in this early learning wipe clean book:

- Look at the pictures and read the words out loud
- Copy the words next to the pictures
- Trace over the doing words in the boxes
- Talk about the describing words on the page

Includes a wipe clean pen so you can practise the words again and again!

Also available in the series:

£4.99

Brown Watson
ENGLAND LE8 0HG

WIP17-20 (Book 3)

ISBN 978-0-7097-2707-1

9 780709 727071